Ghost Writer

*Who among us has not committed
treason to something or someone more
important than a country?*
Graham Greene

*When sorrows come, they come not single spies
But in battalions.*
Hamlet

Ghost Writer
A Novel in Verse

Andy Croft

Five Leaves Publications
www.fiveleaves.co.uk

Ghost Writer
Andy Croft

Published in 2008 by Five Leaves Publications,
PO Box 8786, Nottingham NG1 9AW
info@fiveleaves.co.uk
www.fiveleaves.co.uk

ISBN: 978 1 905512 38 6

Five Leaves gratefully acknowledges financial support
from Arts Council England

The author would like to acknowledge the financial
support of a New Writing North Time to Write Award
and of the Cultural Sector Development Initiative.

Five Leaves is a member of Inpress Books
(www.inpressbooks.co.uk),
representing independent publishers

Designed and typeset by Four Sheets Design and Print
Printed in Great Britain

Dedication

For John and Pauline Lucas

The dedication of a novel
Should be a place to shout and sing,
And yet I feel I ought to grovel
For asking you to read the thing.
The Pushkin stanza – if I'm candid –
Is hard work, awkward, heavy-handed,
Unsuited to the English tongue,
The lines too short, the rhymes too long.
In Russian, rhymes are ten-a-penny,
Unlike our uninflected nouns;
Our trochee-rhymes will jump for clowns
But not for lovers like Yevgeny;
This sonnet's more like chess than verse,
3-D Sudoku, only worse.

You may suspect I'm talking twaddle
And that this verse-form's fried my brains,
And yet I like it as a model
For preaching while it entertains.
I hope you'll grant me, then, permission
To wear an antic disposition
As Hamlet did, with method in't,
And act, at times, the Fool in print.
The form that danced for Tatyana's
Less subtle than a *Viz* cartoon,
More obvious than a moon in June.
It may in fact be quite bananas,
But as you know, in English Lit.,
The straight-jacket's a natural fit.

The other reason I've re-booted
These unheroic, slapstick rhymes
Is that the stanza seems so suited
To our grave and clownish times.
Although my author is too sodden
To know he's dead – *c'est très* Post-Modern! –
It wasn't *Tod* who slipped the knife
Between the ribs of art and life.
I hope therefore you will not quarrel
With my attempt to make the point
That still the time is out of joint,
Or argue with my simple moral
That we still need that good old cause,
Which – like this little book – is yours.

Contents

Dramatis Personae

Tod Prince	*A young biographer*
Rex Dedman	*A 1930's poet, now deceased*
Trudi Dedman	*Rex's wife, also deceased*
John Rackstraw	*A communist, killed in the Spanish Civil War*
Claud King	*Tod's publisher, who fought with Dedman and Rackstraw in Spain*
Fee	*Tod's long-suffering girlfriend*
Derek	*A clown*

Chapter 1

The actors are come hither
Hamlet II.2

'Tis now struck twelve, the world is sleeping, **Tod**
There's nothing stirring, not a mouse; **Prince**
The only sound's the sodden weeping **at his**
That shudders, ghost-like, through the house; **desk**
And as the sobbing slowly passes
Among the ashtrays, plates and glasses,
The blinking minutes of the night
Are counted by computer-light.
The scene is set, the mood is mostly
Suggestive of the tragic art.
Our hero, Tod, is sick at heart,
His candle-life now flickers, ghostly,
Pursued by phantoms which, it seems,
Must haunt him even in his dreams.

Where others dream of sex and money, **Tod's**
Of life as one long endless cruise, **Life**
Tod's dreams consist of darker honey –
Of Sunday Supplement reviews,
The Book at Bedtime, Libby Purves,
The South Bank Show, the old World Service.
Ten years ago Tod said that he
Would turn his useless PhD
Into a Waterstone's best-seller.
But in the disappointments since,
Our author – whose full name's Tod Prince –
Has watched his green hopes turn to yellow,
Just like the bills upon the mat
Inside this weary, stale, old flat.

It once seemed such a good idea!
An easy way to make a splash,
The kick-start to a bright career,
The quickest route to fame and cash.
The Thirties being then in season
It seemed to Tod there was no reason
His shouldn't join the breeze-block Lives
On which the British book trade thrives.
The major names already taken
(Woolf, Auden, Swingler, Barker, Joyce),
Tod faced a somewhat narrowed choice;
His chance of bringing home the bacon
Depended on some long-lost Red,
Once widely read, now safely dead.

Prolific poet, if somewhat minor,
Rex Dedman seemed to be Tod's chance.
He'd fought in Spain and been to China,
Wrote thrillers published by Gollancz,
First joined the YCL at Eton,
Was photographed by Cecil Beaton,
Produced some rather minor verse
And minor travel books (no worse
Than anything by Stephen Spender),
Was read in *Left Review* and *Fact*
Until the Nazi-Soviet Pact,
Then spent the Fifties on a bender.
A writer – critics all agree –
Whose life was in a minor key.

**Rex
Dedman**

But ten years on and Tod's no nearer
To banking any royalty cheques;
With every floppy disk it's clearer
He'll not complete his life of Rex.
The usual stumbling-block of course is
A lack of proper primary sources;
But there's *too* much in Dedman's case,
So much on poor Tod's database –
Unpublished novels, letters, speeches,
Unfinished plays, libretti, notes.
Tod trawls them all in search of quotes
As if somehow convinced that each is
Potentially the final clue
He needs to make his portrait true.

And yet, despite such fond devotion,
The archivist's slow, patient art,
Tod can't resist the growing notion
He knows less now than at the start.
As he collects the jig-saw pieces
His sense of Rex somehow decreases,
As if he must have somehow skipped
A crucial dog-eared manuscript.
What's worse, the more that Tod discovers
About his subject's private life,
The complications with a wife
And endless mistresses and lovers,
The more he struggles to suppress
The thought he likes Rex less and less.

Ten years have passed, ten years of worry.
Flat broke, no girlfriend and depressed –
To say that Tod is in a hurry
To get the damn thing off his chest
Is something of an understatement.
But there's no prospect of abatement.
This very witching time of night
He's still awake and trying to write.
Behold the author now composing –
With nothing but occasional sups
Of lukewarm beer and endless cups
Of cold black tea to stop him dozing
Just long enough to realize
He'll never get the glittering prize…

… 'And so, we reach the nominations
For this year's Boswell Prize, for works
Of monumental paginations –'
The chat-show host looks up and smirks:
'*My Humble Path,* by Julie Burchill,
Wayne Rooney's life of Winston Churchill,
The Answer's No, by Germaine Greer,
And Irvine Welsh's new *Top Gear…*'
'The literary life!' our hero's thinking,
One hand around a champagne flute,
One arm around a rather cute
Young editor with whom he's drinking.
He hopes that if he's not too pissed
She'll maybe add him to her list.

**A writer's
dreams**

A former actress from *Eastenders*
Is played on stage and takes the mike
(She's wearing nothing but suspenders,
A fact the crowd appears to like)
Accompanied by a Chelsea goalie.
'It's now our pleasure –' she reads slowly…
Tod realizes something's wrong,
But as in dreams, has lost his tongue.
Dramatic pause. 'And this year's winner –'
'But wait!' Tod tries to shout, 'Hang on,
My Life is missing – where's it gone?'…
He wakes to find his TV dinner
Is smeared like blood across the page
He'd printed in a bloodless rage.

Tod rubs his eyes and looks around him;
The trappings and the suits of woe
(His dirty washing) still surround him.
This nightmare never stops. And so
He brings to life his old computer
And watches as his persecutor
Materializes like a ghost:
That haunting shot from *Picture Post*
Somewhere in Spain – pure propaganda,
But still effective all the same:
The handsome face, the eyes aflame
With unembarrassed boyish candour.
Tod sighs, clicks on and starts to read
The pages of computer-screed.

**Tod
tries
to
work**

'Let's see, where was I? Chapter 7,
Where Dedman volunteers for Spain;
When to be young was very heaven
And nothing was the same again.
In early '38 he travelled
To Paris where, it seems, he cavilled
At Party discipline. While there,
He had a passionate affair
With Sally Bowles (the *Daily Worker*);
Apparently he disappeared
For fourteen days. The Party feared
The worst, of course, but sometime *circa*
Late Feb he's seen with Claud and John
On board a train to Carcassonne...'

... The picture fades. Cue railway creaking,
French landscape shot in monochrome,
Three Englishmen, afraid of speaking
Of their adventure far from home.
One seems to find the whole thing boring.
One's fast asleep and calmly snoring.
The third is staring into space,
A stern expression on his face.
'Are you all right, John? You're not blinking.'
John smiles: 'The Struggle's like this train
That's taking us to fight in Spain.
We can't get off, it's no good thinking
This is a holiday, eh Rex?'
Rex shuts his eyes and thinks of sex.

Somewhere
near the
Franco-
Spanish
border
early
1938

14

'The express train of Revolution!'
'A shame that there's no buffet-car.'
'We all must make our contribution'
'And I must find the nearest bar.'
'You know, the Party's not a party,
A picnic for the literati.'
'Yes, quite,' says Rex, 'I'm sure you're right,
I've eaten nothing since last night!'
'That's not the point, Rex, please stop joking.'
'I think,' Rex smiles, 'we're slowing down,
Yes look, we've reached the frontier town.'
He lifts his bag down, roughly poking
Their sleeping friend. 'For heaven's sake,
Look here old chap, it's time to wake!'...

... 'Wake up, wake up!' 'I'm – what the bloody –   **Tod is**
I mean just who the hell are you?   **visited**
What are you doing in my study?   **by Rex**
It's – oh my God! It can't be true!'   **Dedman's**
'Wake up old chap.' 'Am I still dreaming?   **ghost**
Please go away or I'll start screaming.'
'To sleep, perchance to dream,' 'To what?'
'I said – oh never mind – I've got
Some news for you, so stop pretending.'
'This isn't happening, let me out!'
'Oh come on man, and please don't shout,
My life requires a different ending;
I am thy father's spirit, Tod.'
'You're not my father – you're – oh God! –

Rex Dedman! Long-lost thirties figure,
Bohemian and sometime Red,
Remembered for his sexual vigour
And not the books that no-one's read;
Who spent the War in bars in Cairo
Defeating Hitler with your biro.
The Cold War left you in the lurch
And flirting with the Catholic Church,
A kind of intellectual gypsy,
A broken-hearted commissar
Whose only home was at the bar,
Who half the time was more than tipsy,
A broken reed, a fading red,
'You can't scare me – because you're dead!'

'A bar-fly *and* a minor poet –   **They**
Aha, the flattery of Youth!'   **argue**
'You blew it, Dedman, and you know it,
It only hurts 'cos it's the truth.'
'If pain's to be truth's only measure
Dishonesty must be a pleasure!
I am thy father's spirit Tod,'
'But how can –' 'It's a quote – dear God!
I thought you were some kind of writer.
You know, old chap, you really ought
To read a bit. Fact is, I thought
I might deserve – well – someone brighter.'
Rex points to the computer screen:
'It's got to stop. My Life, I mean.'

'It *has* stopped, Rex! Or can't I mention
The fact that you're *already* dead?'
'Dear boy, for God's sake, pay attention
To what I'm saying. When I said
It's got to stop, I meant this scribble –'
'It's typed!' 'For Heaven's sake, don't quibble.
Look here, old chap, d'you think I could?'
Rex pours a drink. 'Perhaps I should
Explain the purpose of my visit.
You see – you don't mind if I smoke?'
'Are ghosts allowed?' 'Is that a joke?
It's hardly going to kill me, is it?'
Rex lights a small cigar and grins,
'Cue Bach, I think,' and then begins.

'I want it published, Tod, and quickly,
In time for next year's Christmas list.'
'List, list, oh list!' – Tod's voice comes thickly –
'One little fact you may have missed
Is that I'm stuck on chapter 20 –
"The Glue-pot Years" (and there were plenty)'.
'And good times too. Look here, old son,
I'm here to help you get it done.
But first I want some changes making.'
'Like what?' 'Well, cutting out the part
Regarding Sally for a start.'
Tod's angry now and no mistaking:
'What's done is done. To be exact
Your life's not fiction – it's a fact!

I've read her papers, Rex, come off it,
She wrote about your fling – at *length*.'
'How flattering. But there's no profit
In arguing.' 'But –' 'Give me strength!
It never happened, and I'll prove it,
That's why I want you to remove it.
Less matter and more art, I think,
Is what's required.' Rex sinks his drink.
'Now look, I've made a few enquiries,
And Claud King's memoirs will be out
By Christmas, tedious stuff no doubt
(The man kept all those bloody diaries).
I mean to rain on his parade
And have my dull revenge.' *To fade...*

... The crowing of the cock. Tod's woken
By Nature's early morning call.
He crashes out of bed, a broken,
Pathetic figure still in thrall
To last night's dreaming. As he wonders
If he should see a shrink, he chunders,
Then finds his way without his eyes
Back to his freezing bed and tries
To warm himself. The sheets get chillier.
'I might as well,' he thinks, 'be dead.'
But there's a package on the bed
Addressed to him; the hand's familiar.
He tears it open in a rage
And starts to read the opening page...

Chapter 2

Of each new-hatch'd, unfledg'd comrade. Beware
Hamlet I. 3

... *'Feb 7. I'm writing by the river,*
Across the square from Notre Dame.
T's left me here to sit and shiver
While she sends Pa a telegram
Requesting cash. Now she's consented
To be my mistress, we have rented
A room behind the Gare du Nord.
It's bloody cold, of course, but more
Importantly, it's cheap. We ration
Ourselves to one hot meal per day –
Same onion soup, same old café,
Then warm ourselves at night with passion
(At least that's free) – La Vie Bohème
On love and onions per diem!

If any of the boys could see me
They wouldn't know the Rex of old:
I play Rodolfo to her Mimi
(Her little hands are always cold!)
Sweet girl. 'O soave fanciulla'
This woman is my heart's one ruler.
Sod politics – I much prefer
To warm the world by loving her.
I think this time I'm truly smitten –
Check-mate, clean-bowled and I don't care,
Hook, line and sinker. I declare
No love poem I have ever written
Compares to how we rhyme each night
When we make love by candle-light.

From
Rex's
diary,
early
1938,
Paris

The trouble is, now we are lovers,
It's more than just one amour.
Most girls, once got beneath the covers,
Turn out to be a bloody bore.
But Trudi's loving is so tender,
(No problem there!) with each surrender
She leaves me feeling quite unmanned.
This really isn't what I'd planned.
Each night I watch her sleeping sweetly,
The image of all womankind,
Her jealous lover left behind.
Dear God, I want this girl completely!
I'm going down, all hands on decks,
Content to drown. Alas, poor Rex.

Feb 12. Last night when we had eaten,   **Enter John**
John Rackstraw came in here with Claud.   **Rackstraw**
I knew John when we were at Eton,   **and**
The kind of boy we all adored,   **Claud King**
A head of house (but not a hearty).
At Trinity he joined the Party.
He's spent the last three months in Spain.
I think the whole thing quite insane.
That's not to say I'm not disgusted
With Britain's undisguised support
For General Franco and his sort;
But more that I'm too well adjusted
To want to dig a hero's grave.
In other words, not very brave.

20

John's desperate to rejoin the fighting,
To do his bit to help the cause.
He finds the thought of war exciting,
'To be a part of History's Laws'.
I would have said that he'd be smarter
Than trying to play the bloody martyr,
But God knows what Claud's doing here,
Or what John sees in him (I fear
Their friendship isn't just fraternal).
A tiresome, wart-infested chap,
Who wears a comic dustman's cap
And lugs around a secret journal.
What does he find to write about?
I rather think I should find out.

Feb 15. Wish I could stop sneezing.
Long talk with John about the War.
His diagnosis isn't pleasing;
He says this show's the overture
To greater wars which may be global.
No doubt Democracy is noble,
An honourable and just ideal,
But people die in wars for real ;
God knows I'm not in any hurry
To shed my life-blood for the cause
In this or any other wars.
John says we really shouldn't worry,
We're all forgotten when we've gone.
Sometimes I wish I were like John.

Feb 17. It's started sleeting.
I'm writing this in our café.
John's off to find some factory meeting.
T's reading from L'Humanité.
Each day the news from Spain is grimmer,
The chance of victory's getting slimmer.
Meanwhile old Claud has disappeared.
Since he arrived he's grown a beard
(He thinks it makes him look Hispanic)
The strange thing is, not even John
Appears to know where Claud has gone.
I hardly think we need to panic;
I don't care what the creature does
So long as he stays clear of us.

Feb 21. This morning, dozing,
Post-coital with T in bed,
I somehow found myself proposing
Before I realised what I'd said.
'Oh Rex – you are so sweet,' she parried,
'Imagine us two being married!
You sometimes say the funniest things.'
And that was that. What really stings
Is that she thought I wasn't serious.
The Hairy Warthog has returned!
Bad news as far as I'm concerned.
The fellow's acting all mysterious;
Asked where he's been, he winks, pretends
That he's been looking up old friends.

**A
proposal**

22

Tonight was our last night. They're leaving
Tomorrow on the morning train.
We're still pretending, half-believing
Democracy will win in Spain.
Although of course we raised our glasses
In honour of the working-classes –
'Aux Armes!' 'Red Front!' 'No Passaran!'
'Tovarishi!' 'The Five Year Plan!' –
Our slogans somehow lacked conviction.
We know the future can't be planned,
All we can do is make a stand.
This war is not a Boy's Own fiction.
T looked at me tonight as though
She knows something that I don't know.

Feb 24. The stars are dying.
T's sleeping in our narrow bed.
I've sat up half the night, still trying
To find the words that must be said.
The letter's finished. Almost morning.
Oh God I'm tired. I can't stop yawning.
This is my way to make her see
How much my darling means to me.
I know she'll say that I'm misguided,
But I'm as serious as John.
When she reads this I'll be long gone.
My mind's made up. I have decided.
This morning I'll be on that train.
I'm going with John and Claud to Spain...

Rex takes a decision

… As Claud King puts down Dedman's diary,
Tod watches him across the desk ;
His hairy warts now grey and wiry,
Tod finds him really quite grotesque.
King takes his glasses off and pauses,
'You realise this "find" of yours is
A very clever counterfeit.
It almost fooled me, I admit;
The tone of petulant self-pity
Is Dedman to a T, all right,
But Trudi wasn't there that night,
She wasn't even in the city.'
'Then why did he – ?' 'Let me explain
Why Dedman really went to Spain.'

In the
offices
of Claud
King,
Tod's
publisher

King picks up Dedman's Paris journal
And drops it gently in the bin.
'You won't,' he says, the smile paternal,
'Be needing this.' He rubs his chin.
'The truth is rather less romantic.
I know that this will sound pedantic,
But *I was there*, and I intend
To spill the beans about our friend.
I'll let you have the detailed data
That demonstrates your precious Rex,'
King stops to fiddle with his specs,
'Was just another well-heeled traitor.'
'A what?' 'A *spy*, one of the moles
She put in place.' 'Who?' 'Sally Bowles.

24

It seems that Rex was first recruited
At Cambridge with the other spies ;
Turns out that he was rather suited
To cloak-and-dagger work – the guise
Of useless poet and demon lover
Soon proved to be a useful cover.
But Dedman didn't fool old Claud.
I knew at once he was a fraud.
But just what kind I found out later,
When we attacked Hill 481.
That was the last time I saw John.
I swear that I'll expose the traitor;
I owe it to my friends whose bones
Were left beneath those Spanish stones.'

'It can't be true,' cries Tod, 'you're lying,
I don't believe a single word.
The thought of Rex involved in *spying*!
The whole idea is too absurd.'
King sighs and gazes at the ceiling,
'Forgive me if I speak with feeling,
But I don't give a flying fuck
What you believe: you'll change your book
To show Rex working for the Russians.'
'But if –' 'No buts, I'll have my way,
You'll do exactly as I say.
There may be legal repercussions,
But nothing that we can't afford.
And anyway we're well insured.'

Tod feels the walls around him closing,
The ground beneath him starts to shake.
It can't be true – but just supposing
His research is one long mistake?
Has he misunderstood completely
The life he thought he'd filed so neatly?
Could he have Rex entirely wrong?
At last our hero finds his tongue:
'But even if he *was* disloyal,
Can you imagine what this means?
Your sudden need to spill the beans
On Rex's life is going to spoil
My life of Dedman at a stroke –
Ten years of *my* life up in smoke!'

King stares at Tod as if debating
To have him beaten up or killed.
'Your loyalty is fascinating –
I really thought you would be thrilled.
I hardly think I need remind you
How long it is since we first signed you;
And anyway, it's plain to see
You want Rex dead as much as me.
You hate the bastard with a passion.
No problem. Finding long-dead Reds
Between the sheets *and* under beds
Is quite the literary fashion.
You want him dead? This is your chance.
What's more,' King smiles, 'here's your advance.'

Tod takes the cheque and starts to tremble –
It's flourished with a line of noughts.
He's briefly struck how they resemble
The line of Claud King's hairy warts.
King's talking now of media lunches,
The Boswell Prize, 'You know, my hunch is
Your Life of Rex will be big news.
Imagine Tod, the interviews
With Melvyn, Mark and Mariella!
We'll really give the book a push
In time to catch the Christmas rush;
The book's a guaranteed best-seller,
Just think about it, Tod – *Red Rex*:
A life of treachery *and* sex!

'We'll bring the book out late September,
With Book Club tie-ins, Tod, *the works*.
By then, of course, you may remember,
My memoirs will be out,' King smirks,
'A pincer movement, Tod – between us
We'll take old Dedman to the cleaners.'
Tod barely hears as King explains
His plans for marketing campaigns
Involving Dick and Dom, Paul Morley,
Pete Doherty and Andrew Marr,
Well-placed reviews by Jimmy Carr,
The Hitchens, Ant and Dec, Sue Lawley –
Before he can hear any more
Our fainting hero hits the floor…

… Tod's sitting at his desk, now tidied
Of all its ash-trays, cups and cans.
The copious notes that King's provided
Are by his side. He closely scans
The elegant, hand-written pages
As if they represent his wages.
He makes a note of every date
Marked January '38.
Part Simenon, part Raymond Chandler,
He lists the bars in which Rex boozed,
Dead-letter boxes which he used,
The gardens where he met his handler,
The girls with whom he spent his nights –
Rex Dedman, traitor – banged to rights!

Jan '38? Must be an error.
King wasn't there till early Feb.
Then how did he – ? Tod stops in terror.
He's caught inside a spider's web.
If not Claud King, then who was spying
On Rex in Paris? Was King lying
About the date when they first met?
Or did he really just forget?
Who was betrayed and who the traitor
In Paris 1938?
Tod feels the sticky web vibrate.
He knows he's not a mere spectator
In this strange version of I Spy.
But who's the spider, who the fly?

Chapter 3

The worm that hath eat of a king
Hamlet IV.3

The night is cold, the air bites shrewdly,
The curtain moves. How now! A rat?
Too cold for rats – to put it crudely,
Tod can't afford to heat his flat,
And anyway, all rats are daunted
When they believe a house is haunted.
This midnight, as in Elsinore,
The graves stand tenantless once more.
O ministers of grace defend us!
A figure switches on the light
And sits at Prince's desk. Tonight
The dead pursue their own agendas;
Not for the first time, Dedman's wife
Has come to tidy up his Life.

'My God, it's like some weird museum –
Just look at all these photographs!
What Rex would say, if he could see 'em,
I hate to think,' the figure laughs;
'That funny head by Gordon Herickx
Which always had us in hysterics,
Gabe's famous cartoon in *Our Time*
Promoting Rex's pantomime
For Unity, his book on Lorca,
The page-proofs of his Life of Pepys –
My God, this place gives me the creeps,
This student Prince is like a stalker!'
She lights herself a cigarette,
'I really think it's time we met.'

Tod's empty flat is visited by the ghost of Trudi Dedman

29

She runs her smoky fingers gently
Along the books now foxed with age
And picks out one which accidentally
Falls open at the title page,
John Rackstraw's slim *To Break the Fetters*:
'For R and T, onlie begetters
Of my first book. Your comrade, J'.
'Dear John,' she thinks, and looks away
As if to stop herself from crying.
'You died when you were just a kid,
And nothing that you ever did
Was quite so famous as your dying.
The truest of us all – but who
Will ever write a life of you?'

She grabs the mouse and starts to grapple
With Tod's museum-piece machine;
She brings to life the ancient Apple
And scrolls the text upon the screen:
'In late December '37
He left his parents' house in Devon
And caught the boat-train via Dunkerque
To Paris where he started work
As Moscow's agent (code-name 'Boris')
Among the British volunteers
En route to Spain. It now appears
His contacts there were Arthur Norris
And Sally Bowles. While he was there
It seems they had a brief affair...'

'A Soviet agent! How amusing!
Is this some kind of stupid joke?
My husband was too busy boozing
To get involved in any cloak-
And-dagger stuff. A fornicator
He may have been, but not a traitor.
Where did the fellow get this junk?
My husband was a faithless drunk
But does this really need repeating?
This kind of thing is overplayed.
The only cause that Rex betrayed
Was me.' She sighs, and starts deleting
The references to Sally Bowles
Till chapter 7 is full of holes.

'Now let me see,' she frowns, 'supposing
We cut and paste a name or two?'
One-fingeredly she starts transposing
King's name with Dedman's. 'That should do
The trick,' she smiles. 'This is your actual
So-called postmodern counterfactual!
If History's a palimpsest
Then who can say whose truth is best?
It all depends upon your angle.
But anyway, now that's removed
I think he'll find it much improved.'
As if on cue she hears the jangle
Of fumbled keys outside the door
And singing in the corridor.

Tod stumbles in, somewhat unsteady.
Although he is far gone, far gone,
Tonight our Prince is more than ready
To pour himself another one.
He takes the bottle from the table
Then freezes. 'What? How were you able – ?
Oh not again! I may be pissed
But I know phantoms don't exist.
This isn't happening – I won't let it.
Hold, hold my heart! If you think I'm
About to let you waste my time
Discussing books you can forget it.
Please go away – I don't care how
But please, please, please, just *fuck off* now!'

Enter Tod
in his cups

'You must be Tod,' the ghost announces,
'I don't think we've been introduced.'
'Well I know you all right,' Tod pounces,
'You're Trudi Dedman! And you used,
Like most stiffs, to be six feet under.
It really isn't any wonder
I think I'm going off my head –
I spend my evenings with the dead.'
Tod's sense of panic's rising steeply.
'I've got it now,' he starts to shake,
'I'm starring in a cheap remake
Of *Truly Madly Bloody Deeply*!
You brought your cello? I suppose
You'll want to watch some videos?'

They argue

'Been celebrating?' Trudi queries.
'You bet I have,' Todd lights a fag,
'I'm done with literary bloody theories,
Your husband's finished, in the bag.
My publisher's already hinting
It's going to need a second printing.'
'I'm not surprised,' Ms Dedman smiles,
'Among us long dead bibliophiles
Your book has caused no small commotion.'
'I beg your pardon?' 'Oh come on,
You don't stop reading when you're gone;
In fact, it's thanks to your devotion
That Rex's work's so widely read
Among the literary dead.'

'Yeah, well,' Tod sneers, 'I'll make a killing
Exposing Dedman as a fake.'
'And are you, Tod?' 'What?' 'Are you willing
To rat on Rex?' 'For pity's sake!
Ten years I've wasted on the bastard,
And only recently I've mastered
The man at last – a traitor who
Betrayed us all, especially you.'
'Look Tod, you made of Rex an idol
And when you found his feet were clay
Declared that you had been betrayed.
So please don't come all patricidal.
I've seen that Judas lake of ice –
Believe me, Tod, it isn't nice.

You made of Rex a father figure
Whose manhood had to be destroyed.
It's penis-envy, Tod – don't snigger –
A classic case, straight out of Freud.
Pen-envy too, since as a writer
You envy Rex.' 'I hate the blighter!'
'My point exactly, Tod – don't scoff –
That's why you want to kill him off.
It's you who are the traitor, sonny,
"The King is dead – long live the King!"
If Rex had the occasional fling
At least it wasn't done for money.
Your book's a form of *regi*cide!'
'But Trudi – he's already died!

Is Richard Holmes or D.J. Taylor
Pursued by phantoms in the night?
Do poltergeists tell Norman Mailer
And Andrew Morton what to write?
I see dead people Doc, no really –
They're all my friends, I love them dearly.'
'Look Tod, if that's your attitude –'
'What do you want then, gratitude?
Pull up a chair, let's have a natter –
I've Jacob bloody Marley's ghost
Inside my flat and I'm supposed
To act as though it doesn't matter!
Oh God, it's doing in my head,
Why won't dead people just stay dead?'

'Because the past is still important ;
Although we're dead, that's not to say
We're not *involved*, or that we oughtn't
To want to change things. Anyway,'
She puts an arm round Prince's shoulder,
'You'll understand when you are older
Something the dead have always known:
That history's never set in stone.
You see,' she points to Tod's computer,
'I've made some changes here and there –'
'You've what?' Tod yelps, 'that isn't fair!'
He looks as if he wants to shoot her,
But staggers to the fridge, 'I think
It's time I had another drink.

I don't care if I am a traitor,
It's not your husband's life – it's mine,
He's mine to kill – I'm his creator –'
'O spare us Dr Frankenstein.'
'Exposing Rex will make him famous!'
'Stop acting like an ignoramus!'
'I know Claud King's a funny sort
But –' *'Who*?' 'Claud King'. 'The Hairy Wart?'
'My publisher – I thought you knew him.'
'Oh yes, I knew Claud King all right,
The creeping Paris parasite.
You know he wanted me to screw him?
Came crawling round when Rex was ill,
A vulture waiting for a kill'...

... Accordion music. Café table.
Some snow. A pre-war Paris street.
A handsome woman wrapped in sable.
A man arrives and takes a seat.
They order coffee. 'Well, what is it?'
'You know, this coffee's quite exquisite –'
'Look, stop it Claud, stop acting weird.'
The man just smiles and strokes his beard
And hums the Internationale.
'What's going on? What's this about?'
'Calm down old girl, no need to shout.'
'Please stop behaving so bizarrely
And tell me why you've brought me here.'
'If you insist. Du lait, my dear?'

He sips his coffee. 'I'll be candid,
I've never really liked the bloke,
His attitude's so damned high-handed,
I know he thinks that I'm a joke.
I hate these left-wing upper-classes.'
He stops to fiddle with his glasses.
'But now I know the sordid truth –
Trust good old Claud to play the sleuth –
About our famous Casanova.'
He smirks and strokes his hairy moles.
'Look Claud, if you mean Sally Bowles,
You don't scare me; that's long been over.
I know there's nothing going on.'
'Not Fraulein Bowles you goose – with John!'

The woman sits there, unbelieving.
'With John? But that's – it can't be true!'
'My dear, there's really no point grieving,
The question is, what will you do?
You want someone you can rely on,
A friendly shoulder you can cry on.'
He reaches out to take her hand.
'You're shocked old girl, I understand,
But soon I doubt you'll even miss him.
You need a place to stay tonight,
And good old Claud will see you right...'
The woman stands as if to kiss him
Then slaps his face and turns to go.
Accordion music. Falling snow...

Somewhere outside a cock is crowing
That is the trumpet to the morn.
'Look, Tod, it's time that I was going,'
Says Trudi, swallowing a yawn,
'But I'll be back, perhaps tomorrow.
Till then I thought you'd like to borrow
This story – catch!' She throws it him.
'It's written under pseudonym,
First published in *Penguin New Writing*,
Soon after Lehmann went to Lane.
As you will see, it's set in Spain.
Though hardly what you'd call exciting,
I know it was the work of John.
Enjoy it, Tod.' And then she's gone.

The title's framed by wild cross-hatches
Where someone's doodled in red ink.
It's called 'A King of Shreds and Patches'.
Tod pours himself another drink,
Begins to read the introduction
And falls at once for the seduction
Of Audenesque *roman à clef* ;
The editor explains that 'J
Was lost in action near Corbrera.
Some time before he died he penned
This story which a loyal friend,
Then serving as a stretcher-bearer,
Brought back with him from Spain last year.
New Writing's proud to print it here.'

The story's Thirties documentary,
Part André Malraux, part Ralph Bates,
Hard-hitting prose, but rudimentary,
The sort of stuff Tod usually hates,
All olive-grove and sunburned torso,
Like Hemingway, but even more so.
But this time Tod is not amused.
The main protagonist's accused
Of sabotage, of being a traitor,
Provocateur and Carlist spy ;
What really catches Prince's eye
Though, is the fact that the narrator
Describes the man he calls 'El Roy'
As sometimes known as 'Warty Boy'.

Chapter 4

A consummation devoutly to be wished
Hamlet III.1

'Two pilau rice, one chicken balti,   **Tod is**
And – let me see – one vindaloo,   **celebrating**
Some taka daal – but not too salty –
A garlic naan – no, make that two.
And popadoms, please, while we're waiting.'
Tonight our hero's celebrating.
The reason is, Tod's free at last,
No longer haunted by the past,
By nightly fears and daily worries.
He's finally exorcised the ghost –
The book is done, and in the post.
But while they're waiting for their curries
Tod wonders what Claud King will think.
The bastard's bound to cause a stink.

Incredibly, Tod has persuaded   **Fee**
A girl he sometimes used to date
(For whom his passion hasn't faded)
To come and help him celebrate.
When he recalls his long and lonely
Devotion to the dead, his only
Commitment now's to feel alive!
Just then their popadoms arrive.
The girl (her name is Fee)'s a teacher;
She's from the local convent-school.
Tod knows that he has been a fool
When he regards the lovely creature
Across the table, tucking in
With mango chutney on her chin.

The problem was, when they were dating,
Tod's head was full of Dedman quotes.
So many times he kept Fee waiting
While he stayed in to type his notes.
She said their friendship was abortive;
He said that she was unsupportive;
She said he couldn't give her love
And so she gave poor Tod the shove.
But now he's left all that behind him
And finally put down his pen,
Tod hopes that they can try again.
In fact, five lagers have inclined him
To think this dinner with his ex-
Might even end (who knows?) with sex.

If they're to make a new beginning,
The moment's come to make his move.
He throws a smile he hopes is winning,
To get the lady in the groove;
This is the time to grasp the metal,
To show the girl he's on his nettle.
While waiters clear away their plates
Our would-be lover hesitates
Then takes Fee's hand and softly squeezes;
He feels the thumpings of their hearts;
'O Fee,' he sighs, but as he starts
To stroke her finger-ends, she freezes –
His mobile phone's begun to ring.
Tod answers it. Bad move – it's King.

To say King's not a happy bunny
Would not do justice to his mood.
He's ranting on about his money
And Prince's moral turpitude,
Accusing Tod of being a traitor,
The worst kind of tergiversator.
'Look, Claud, it's not a good time now –'
But King is making such a row
That Tod's attracting funny glances
From other couples, 'Sorry Claud –'
While Fee is looking tired and bored.
'You're breaking up.' Tod knows the chances
That they will end up in the sack
Are fading fast. ' I'll ring you back...'

**Tod takes
a phone-
call from
King**

Tod switches off, tries looking cheerful,
But knows that Fee won't let it be;
He's going to get another earful:
'Oh please don't hang up just for me,
I've not had so much fun in ages.
Why don't I get the *Yellow Pages*
So you can ring up all your friends?'
'I'm sorry Fee.' Tod comprehends
If he's to get inside her knickers
It's going to take a change of mood.
He lets the waiters bring their food.
The candle on their table flickers.
Tod takes her wrist and holds her hard:
It's time to play the illness card.

**Fee
is not
pleased**

'I know this won't affect you greatly –
Why should it after all this time? –
But I've not been too well just lately.
The problem is, you see, that I'm,
Well, suffering from hallucinations –
Too much hard work, too few vacations.
My doctor says it's caused by stress.
Oh God! My head is such a mess.
I need someone to give me succour.
I'm sorry Fee, give me a break,'
He blows his nose, 'for old time's sake?'
His trembling lips begin to pucker.
Fee frowns, then smiles, 'OK. Let's go.
Why don't we try and see a show?'

They scan the local evening paper
Which offers them a choice between
An undergraduate Stoppard caper,
A touring *Hamlet* Fee has seen,
And what's billed as a *Mousetrap* send-up.
Not good. It looks as if they'll end up
With coffee and a goodnight kiss.
'Hang on a sec though, look at this:
The Olive Grove – it's hard to credit,
But this is Dedman's long-lost play!
He burned it, or so people say;
I've heard of it, but never read it.
O come on Fee, let's go tonight…'
Fee stares at Tod and sighs. 'All right.'

The play's on at the old arts centre
Behind the shops on Denmark Street.
They get there late, but as they enter
It's clear that they've a choice of seat.
In fact they're somewhat disconcerted
To find the hall is quite deserted.
'You'd think it would be full,' says Tod,
'The first night too. How very odd.'
He takes a mint and starts to suck it,
Then settles down to watch the show.
A figure shuffles down their row;
They stand to let him pass. Oh fuck it!
'I thought I'd find you here,' King grins.
The lights go down. The play begins.

...The curtains rise. Cue railway creaking,
French landscape shot in monochrome,
Three Englishmen, afraid of speaking
Of their adventure far from home.
One seems to find the whole thing boring.
One's fast asleep and calmly snoring.
The third is staring into space,
A stern expression on his face.
It's evidently juvenilia,
Clenched fists, high hopes and bright ideals;
Beyond the clichés though, Tod feels
The scene's increasingly familiar.
He shuts his weary eyes. It seems
He's seen this drama in his dreams...

...'Are you all right, Claud? You're not blinking.'
Claud smiles.' The Struggle's like this train:
We can't get off, it's no good thinking
We're going on holiday to Spain.
Especially when – look, can I trust you?
What I've to say may well disgust you.'
He nods towards the boy asleep;
'You see, Rex, I've been sent to keep
An eye on John for Harry Pollitt.'
'On John?' Rex drops his voice. 'But why?'
'The Party thinks that he's a spy.'
'Impossible!' King taps his wallet:
'These letters Rex – quite genuine –
They prove John's working for Berlin'...

King snarls at Tod. 'Complete invention,
This is a knavish piece of work.'
He pulls a gun, 'Now pay attention!'
It looks like King has gone berserk –
'Don't shoot!' yelps Tod. King gives a snigger,
'It's finished Tod!' and pulls the trigger...
...'It's finished, Tod, come on let's go,
Wake up,' says Fee, 'you've missed the show.'
No sign of King. 'You are surprising,
And after you made all that fuss!
Come on or else we'll miss our bus.'
Outside's a poster advertising
Some tragedy: 'The play's the thing
To catch the conscience of the king.'

'What's wrong Tod?' 'Why?' 'Well, your demeanour
Is that of one loosed out of hell.'
'And so would yours if you'd just seen a –
Oh never mind – I don't feel well.
Perhaps it was that cheap Bengali.'
'I think,' says Fee, 'if you're so poorly,
You ought to be in bed...' She stops
Then kisses Tod full on the chops.
It's hardly worthwhile cataloguing
What happens on the bus-drawn miles,
As like a pair of juveniles
They get down to some top-deck snogging.
The question now's not what occurs,
But whether it's his place or hers.

Back at the flat, Tod fills the kettle
While splashing on some aftershave;
The coffee poured, he's quick to settle
Into the role of passion's slave.
To be quite frank the lad's still hoping
The night will end with more than groping;
He swiftly tidies up the place
And plumps the duvet, just in case.
A round or two of frantic tonguing
And he's a well-oiled love-machine,
A puff'd and reckless libertine.
It seems Fee shares his lustful longing
For very soon our lovers tread
The steep way up to heaven – or bed.

**Tod and
Fee get
it on**

45

Tod lies back, watching Fee undressing
Until she's down to bra and pants;
The poor boy doesn't mind confessing
This fits his idea of romance.
'The bathroom Tod?' 'Just through the study.'
'Don't go away,' she smiles. How could he?
For once he can't believe his luck:
At last, he's going to get a – 'Fuck!'
His mobile phone again. With violence
He smashes it against the wall,
It sputters 'You have one missed call'
Then squeaks and gibbers into silence;
Tod throws the pieces in a drawer
As Fee walks naked through the door.

She snuggles up beneath the covers,
As chaste as ice, as pure as snow.
Our pair are not experienced lovers,
Each hopes their innocence won't show.
Tod tries a few text-book manoeuvres,
He strokes, he whispers, licks and hoovers
Until his neck begins to ache
(He wonders if she's still awake),
Then ups the pace; his hand's now creeping
Upon its slow but urgent quest
Until it reaches her left breast –
Just then the bed-side phone starts bleeping:
'If you pick up that phone,' yells Fee,
'That's it – you've seen the last of me.'

Tod lets it ring for several seconds,
Then switches on the answer-phone.
The rest is silence. Tod now reckons
The two of them are quite alone.
This time when he begins to nibble,
Fee groans like the Cumaean Sybil;
She rolls her eyes and bites her lips,
He bites her ears, she rolls her hips,
Until she meets his tender kisses;
Encouraged by her fluting sighs
Tod slips his hand between her thighs.
It seems to work. 'Fuck me!' she hisses,
('At last,' thinks Tod, 'I'm going to score')
'Fuck me, there's someone's by the door!'

Two shapes approach the lovers' bower;
Fee pulls the duvet to her breast.
'We come most carefully upon your hour –'
'For Christ's sake Rex, I must protest,
You can't just walk in at your leisure!'
'I don't believe we've had the pleasure –'
'And thanks to you two, nor have we!'
Rex offers his right hand to Fee,
'We really ought to get acquainted.'
Fee starts to scream. 'Oh dear, oh dear,
It seems that we're not welcome here.
Good heavens Tod, the poor girl's fainted.
Next time perhaps.' But Tod suspects
There won't be one. 'Just fuck off, Rex!'

*Enter
two
ghosts*

They disappear. Young Fee goes mental.
She punches Tod and grabs her stuff.
'I've clearly made a monumental
Misjudgment, Tod. I've had enough!'
'Oh come on, Fee, don't go all moody.
You know it was just Rex and Trudi.'
'I don't want zombies in my bed!'
'But they're not zombies, Fee – they're *dead*!'
She slams the door. Oh God, how squalid.
It wasn't meant to end like that,
His most miraculous organ flat,
His too, too solid flesh unsolid.
The next day Tod is more than vexed
To find that he's been dumped by txt:

**Tod is
disappointed
in love**

i dunno where u got th'impreshun
grp sex wld b my cup of t
ur clrly suffring from depreshun
u need a doctor, Tod, nt me
lst nite ws so humili8ing
nxt tme u fncy celebr8ing
fnd som1 else to hold yr h&
i 1der if u undrst&
ths tme it is gdby 4eva
wr brking up, ur batrys fl@
& u r actng lk a pr@
as sum1 said: the ?s weva
u wnt 2b or nt 2b
a tossa all ur lfe. x Fee.

Exit Fee

Chapter 5

trains, etc
Hamlet V.1

Twelve months have passed. It's now October.
Tod's flat is looking spick and span,
These days our hero's mostly sober –
O what a piece of work is Man!
Our Prince has, since the last debacle,
Recovered something of his sparkle;
No ghostly visits to record,
He's less depressed, more self-assured.
To please Claud King he has redrafted
His Life of Rex so it conforms
To all the usual Cold War norms.
If Dedman's well and truly shafted
Tod's not about to feel contrite.
It serves the stupid bugger right.

**Tod has
finished
the
book**

These days Tod wonders if he's dreaming.
The book's exceeded all his hopes:
It's launched tonight, at last redeeming
The years spent labouring on the slopes
Of academe. Already orders
Are looking good from Smiths and Borders.
He has to hand it to him, King's
Been very busy pulling strings.
The Boswell short-list! Who'd have thought it?
If only Fee could see him now –
Oh never mind the silly cow.
Perhaps the TV will report it –
He peers along the street once more,
Then steps outside and locks the door.

Of course the sodding lift's not working.
It never is. Tod takes the stairs.
The caretaker as usual's lurking
Outside his cubby-hole. He glares.
Tod knows this look. Alas, poor Derek,
His grave expression's the generic
Bad temper of the concierge.
Tod struggles to suppress an urge
To run, but finds the way impeded.
'Oh hell,' thinks Tod. It's just his luck,
Today of all days to be stuck
While Derek rants. Just what he needed.
The man gives Tod the bloody creeps.
Outside the taxi-driver beeps.

'Er – can't stop now, my taxi's waiting,
Must dash – some other time perhaps?'
The old man stands there, cogitating
While several centuries elapse.
Tod holds his breath; his sphincter tightens;
The old man frowns a bit, then brightens
As if recalling what to say:
'This came for you the other day.'
He fishes in his filthy jacket
(He seems to be a man possessed
Of infinitely grubby vest)
And offers Tod a bulky packet.
No time to go back up again –
He'll take it with him on the train.

Tod barely makes it to the station,
But as he sprints towards the gate,
He finds, to his immense vexation
The London train is running late.
He buys a sandwich and a coffee,
Some cigarettes, a bag of toffee
And this week's *Eye*, which features Rex
On its front cover. Tod reflects
That there is something slightly cheesy
In Dedman-Redman-Bedman jokes,
As though his book's a kind of hoax.
It leaves him feeling rather queasy
(Though this could be the tuna-melt
That's now congealed below his belt).

At last the London train approaches.
Frustrated travellers surge *en masse*
Towards the crowded standard coaches
While Tod slips quietly in first-class.
He puts the packet on the table,
Peels back the tape along the label
And carefully unties the string.
Inside's a little note from King,
'I rather thought your next edition
Might benefit from the enclosed.
Try not to get them too exposed.
Despite their delicate condition,
I'm sure you'll quickly get the gist.'
Tod groans, but how can he resist?

'Dear Trudi, You are such a sweetie –
Your letters were already here
When we arrived at Albacete.
You seem so distant – yet so near.
Our journey here was uneventful
(Though you-know-who seemed quite resentful
When he was told to shave his beard!)
I've no regrets I volunteered,
And though my life may soon be ended,
I know I'd do the same again.
I'm proud to be among such men,
The comrades here are truly splendid;
I'll write about them all anon.
Claud's posting this. Best wishes, John.'

'Dear John, I trust you got the letter
I sent via King Street, as you said.
I wish the news from Spain were better,
I read the lists of dead with dread.
Your book's typed up – heroic labour! –
And presently being read by Faber.
In Shoreditch we've a good campaign
To raise support for Aid for Spain.
Last week we held a public meeting;
Old Harry spoke (that's nothing new!)
He even mentioned Rex and you.
His rhetoric would take some beating.
If you have time, please write to me.
No Passaran! Best wishes, T.'

'Dear girl, I hope this finds you cheerful,
That everything's all right with you.
We (Rex and I) are rather fearful
Our letters are not are getting through.
We're working hard – machine-gun training –
If only C would stop complaining!
Although our spirits are still high,
It's sometimes hard. I can't deny
The situation here's confusing.
You know, I'm glad I'm here with Rex;
Of course, the old boy still affects
To find the whole show quite amusing,
But I know now it's just his way.
You must be proud of him. Yours, J.'

'Dear John, I've still not heard a whistle
From you or Rex since you arrived.
I don't expect a verse epistle –
Just let me know that you've survived.
I'm sorry if I sound a moaner!
You know last year in Barcelona?
Well, someone's trying to cause a stir
About the fighting there last year,
Accusing us of being liars;
The author is some kind of Trot
Who claims the war's a Russian plot.
These bloody 'left-wing' Jeremiahs
(You know the sort) I guarantee
Will end up on the Right. Yours, T.'

'Dear T, It's late, but I'm too tired
To sleep beneath these foreign stars.
Awake, I wonder what's required
To wake up England. This fight's ours –
The war we're fighting's universal;
This Spanish show's a mere rehearsal
For what may prove the final fight
Between Democracy and Might.
There's nothing now to be afraid of –
The issues are so stark and clear –
And when we've finished fighting here
We'll show old England what we're made of.
That's it for now. I'm rambling on.
Will try to write again. Love, John.'

'My dearest John, It seems forever
Since our last night in St Germain.
I've got three jobs now (ain't I clever?)
I fill my days as best I can.
I'm back in London with my family
Just while I'm working for Ted Bramley;
I've got the opportunity
To help back-stage at Unity;
Meanwhile, a friend of Johnny Campbell's
Asked me to work for Inprecorr,
Translating stuff about the war.
O God! This world's a bloody shambles!
One day we're going to set it free –
Till then, be careful. All love, T.'

'My dearest T, No time for writing.
We're heading back towards the front.
We've seen some pretty serious fighting.
In fact, old girl, to be quite blunt,
The last [?] has been bloody tricky.
Our entire sector's looking sticky.
I'm scribbling this inside a truck.
[?]'s lost in action. Rotten luck,
Though some chaps won't be all that sorry;
He somehow [?] the human touch.
I miss your letters very much.
O damn and blast this bloody lorry!
I'm not sure [?] I'm trying to say.
Be brave. No Passaran! Love, J.'

'Dear John, The news from Spain gets bleaker.
The tactics that they now rehearse
On Spanish soil – e.g. Guernica –
They'll use on us next, only worse.
And yet, of course, 'Non-Intervention'
Makes clear that Chamberlain's intention
Is now to let the Fascists win.
How they must love him in Berlin!
Our Government's composed of traitors,
A rotten, British ruling class
Who are content to sell the pass
(C.o.d.) to dictators.
If you have time, please write to me.
I miss you, John. God bless. Love, T.'

'Dear Heart, It seems another era
Since I last saw you from the train,
And yet you never have been nearer
Than you are now. Let me explain.
When Death's so close, there's no concealing
From his black stare your deepest feeling,
And if I don't survive this show
There's something I want you to know:
I love you. *Though you never guessed it,*
I've loved you ever since the day
I saw you in that old café
In St. Germain, though I suppressed it.
Be glad that I am fighting here
For Freedom, Life, and you, my dear.'

'Dear Heart, Last night I slept quite badly;
I dreamed that I was on a train
And you were waving, smiling sadly;
I knew I'd not see you again.
I woke to find that I'd been crying.
I know you're not afraid of dying,
But there is something you should know:
I love you. *There, I've said it. Oh*
I love you. Though I have suppressed it,
I've loved you ever since the day
I saw you in that old café.
I don't suppose you ever guessed it,
But now you know, come back to me.
I love you, John. Be strong. x T.'

The scenes outside the window harden
As fields give way to urban sprawl
Of underpass and terraced garden,
Industrial park and shopping mall.
Tod puts the letters in a folder.
He shivers. Christ, it's getting colder.
Bright-lit suburban stations pass
Reflected in the grubby glass.
He goes to fetch himself a bevy;
The buffet's shut. Their bloody loss.
Five minutes till they reach Kings Cross.
It's pissing down. The sky is heavy.
A wilderness of plastic bags
And multi-hued graffiti tags.

'Excuse me sir, is this seat taken? Enter
Well, well – it's Doktor Frankenstein! Trudi's
Unless I'm very much mistaken ghost
I rather think that these are mine.'
'They're private!' 'Yes I know – I wrote them!'
'Did Rex know, Trudi?' 'Will you quote them?'
'Why shouldn't I?' 'It's not polite.'
'But ghosts can't sue for copyright!'
Heads turn among the railway carriage.
She drops her voice, 'Oh never mind.
Look frankly, Tod, I'm not inclined
To talk to you about my marriage –
You're nothing but a peeping Tom.
Please tell me where you got them from.'

'John never read them. My suspicion
Is Claud was opening Rackstraw's post.
He's saved them for my next edition –'
She looks as if she's seen a ghost.
'That's wonderful, Tod – lost in transit!
Life never works the way one plans it,
But this means that poor John was spared
From knowing just how much I cared.
No thanks to Claud, but this perhaps is
A sort of blessing in disguise.
I'm sure by now you realize
That Rex and I both had our lapses;
Forget what bloody King expects,
I'd rather this was kept from Rex.'

The train pulls into King's Cross station.
Tod stands and turns towards the door.
'A young girl's brief infatuation,
That's all it was, Tod, nothing more.
Rex guessed, I think, when he enlisted,
But as for John – I scarce existed.'
'You mean to say you never knew?'
'Knew what?' 'Look, these were meant for you.
You're right, I had no right to read them.'
She gasps, 'But I don't understand –'
Then recognizes Rackstraw's hand.
'They're yours to keep. I doubt I'll need them.'
Tod leaves her on the empty train
And disappears into the rain.

Chapter 6

The wicked prize itself.
Hamlet III. 3

'The literary life!' our hero's thinking,
One arm around a rather cute
Young editor with whom he's drinking,
One hand around a champagne flute.
She seems to find him quite attractive;
He hopes they'll soon get interactive
Once he has learned to play the game
Of cashing in his new-found fame
For what would be a well-earned shagging.
He pours the girl another drink
And wonders what old Fee would think
If she were here. The usual nagging.
Oh never mind. She's burned her boats.
Tonight Tod's going to get his oats.

The place is packed, as King predicted,
With people from the world of books.
The invitations are restricted
To those with influence, money, looks –
A glittering cast of movers, shakers,
Celeb reviewers, image-makers,
Who wander through the smoky haze
And help themselves to canapés.
Tod still suspects he might be dreaming;
Although he's seen this scene before
At least this time he's pretty sure
He isn't going to wake up screaming.
The cameras flash. The press are here.
Tod pours himself another beer.

King's PR team has been well busy
With readings, book-club deals and rights;
At times our prince feels somewhat dizzy
To find himself at such great heights.
This week he's got a spot on *Parky,*
The Moral Maze with David Starkey,
Then *In Our Time*, *Midweek*, *Front Row*
And next week's *Sharon Osbourne Show*.
King's talking to the *Mail on Sunday*
Who are, it seems, quite keen to run
A feature. Meanwhile in the *Sun*
Exclusive extracts start on Monday:
THE SPY WHO SHAGGED ME: NIGHTS OF SEX
GRENADA-STYLE WITH LOVE RAT REX.

The book's a godsend for red-baiters
Demanding ever tougher laws
To deal with Dedman's heirs – the traitors
Opposed to all the Bush-Blair wars.
It's been reviewed in the *Observer*
With suitable Orwellian fervour
By Richard Littlejohn, no less;
In this week-end's *Sunday Express*
Jim Davidson and Simon Schama
Discuss Tod's debt to Eric Blair;
Meanwhile, King hopes that *Marie Claire*
Will feature Francis Fukuyama
And Chapman Pincher on the role
Of Dedman as a Russian mole.

Tod scruffs his hair, undoes his collar,
Admires the figure in the glass:
The image of a modern scholar
And member of the *Late Show* class,
Designer shades, designer stubble,
A hip gun-slinger out for trouble
Whose eyes are on the Boswell Prize.
Although he tries, he can't disguise
The hope that he is going win it –
This morning's *Guardian* says the odds-
On favourite book this year is Tod's.
Proceedings start at any minute.
He takes his book and marks the page
Then joins Claud King upon the stage.

A former entrant from *X-Factor*
Is played on stage and grabs the mike,
Accompanied by an ex-soap actor
(Or ex-soap actor look-alike).
'It's now my pleasure,' she announces,
While wiggling her curvaceous bounces,
'To introduce two special guys
Both up for this year's Boswell Prize.
Two authors in a long tradition –'
She stops to check her autocue
And licks her lips – 'Tod Prince's new
Rex Dedman: Truant Disposition,
And Claud King's *Honoured in the Breach.*'
King takes the mike to cries of 'Speech!'

'My friends, my friends, I'm deeply flattered
To see so many here tonight.
Being popular has never mattered
To me as much as being right,
But Truth can be a cold vocation;
For years my lonely consolation
Was hoping I could do my part
According to the diarist's art.
They also serve who keep a look-out.
While traitors prospered, I kept *shtum*
Because I knew this day would come.
And now at last, I have my book out.'
He wipes a tear. 'I did my best.
It's up to you to do the rest.

It gives me no small satisfaction
To share this stage with my young friend;
Tod knows that Freedom's no abstraction,
But something which we must defend.
Rex Dedman may be dead – however,
The story that our books endeavour
To tell can speak to us today;
In Britain and the USA
Our enemies are growing stronger;
Though slogans change, don't be misled –
The traitors' flag's still deepest red.
So stay with me a little longer,
And follow me down Memory Lane,
To 1938 and Spain.'

... The picture fades. Cue railway creaking,
French landscape shot in monochrome,
Three Englishmen, afraid of speaking
Of their adventure far from home.
One seems to find the whole thing boring.
One's fast asleep and calmly snoring.
The third is staring into space,
A stern expression on his face.
'Are you all right, Claud? You're not drinking —'
'Oh Jesus Christ, Rex, not tonight!'
'To launch your book and not invite
Your oldest friends – what were you thinking?
Although it hurts, and no mistake,
We'll let you off, for old times' sake.'

Enter
ghosts
of Rex
and
Trudi

King starts to sweat, his hand is shaking,
He dabs his brow and starts again.
What was the point that he was making?
He shuts his eyes and counts to ten.
'The picture fades,' but then he stumbles,
The rest comes out in grunts and mumbles.
As in a dream, King's lost his tongue.
The audience knows that something's wrong
But can't be certain what's the matter.
King's shouting now, and punching air
As if there's someone standing there;
A few, embarrassed, make to scatter
Towards the bar, though most still cling
Like courtiers around their king.

King
loses
the
plot

It's obvious that Rex is plastered.
'Come on, old boy, let's drink a toast!
Oh cheer up, you ungrateful bastard,
Stop looking like you've seen a ghost.'
King swings a punch, but Rex ignores him,
As if such violence simply bores him.
'I've brought some wine – it's Spanish red –'
'You don't exist,' snarls King, 'you're dead!'
He glares at them with naked malice
While Rex tops up a plastic cup,
'Here's to thy health. Come on, drink up.'
King takes it like a poisoned chalice
Then tips it over Trudi's skirt.
She smacks his face, 'I hope that hurt!'

The crowd can't see why King's behaving   **Enter**
Like some demented pugilist.   **Fee**
His fists are up, his speech is raving –
The old chap must be either pissed
Or suffering from senile dementia.
'I say,' says Rex, 'if I might venture,
Are you quite sure you're feeling well?'
'I'll see the pair of you in Hell!'
'And so you shall, though that comes later.
But first we need to get things straight
Regarding Spain in '38.'
'Just keep away, you Commie traitor,
Don't shake your gory locks at me!'
'Wrong play, I think.' Tod turns – it's Fee.

'Oh great!' he thinks, 'just what I needed.
The climax to a perfect night.'
Just when he thought he had succeeded
In putting his old ghosts to flight
They all turn up. Tod realises
He'll never get those glittering prizes.
He doesn't think there's any doubt
That when the news of this gets out
They'll both be dropped like hot potatoes.
King's throwing chairs around the stage
And hectoring the walls in rage,
Accusing them of being traitors.
'Look Claud, be careful with that vase! –'
Too late. Our hero's seeing stars.

Tod blacks out again

When Tod wakes up, his brain is aching.
He's lying on some kind of couch.
His head is sore and no mistaking.
Fee dabs his forehead gently. 'Ouch!'
The inside of his mouth tastes bloody.
They're in some kind of private study
Where King's still kicking up a fuss.
'By all means, Dedman, let's discuss
Your sordid past. I don't give twopence
For what you think,' he strokes his warts,
'The past is dead. But then,' he snorts,
It's time you lot got your comeuppance.'
'What do you mean?' asks Rex. King glares.
'Let's start with Trudi's love affairs.'

King accuses his accusers

65

As though upon a fearful summons
She startles like a guilty thing.
'O Frailty, thy name is woman!'
'S-stop it, Claud,' she starts, but King
Ploughs on: 'While we were busy fighting
Your girlfriend here was busy writing
To someone else.' 'To whom?' 'To John.'
'Oh come on, pull the other one!'
'And that's not all,' King plumps his cushions;
'Those *billets-doux* contained a code
Which when deciphered clearly showed
That she was working for the Russians.'
Rex stares at Trudi, 'Is this true?'
'His cover blown, they murdered – *You*!'

'Well better late, I say, than never,'
John Rackstraw grins, 'Remember me?
Dear Trudi – radiant as ever –
And Rex, old friend, long time no see.
I do so hope I'm not intruding,
It looks to me like you've been feuding.
Do I detect an atmosphere?
Bad blood between old friends. Oh dear.
Forgive me Claud, but you were saying
Something about my death, I think.
Rex, pour our friend another drink,
He looks quite pale. Now let's stop playing.
The Party's sent me to report
On what to do with Hairy Wart.'

**Enter
Rackstraw's
ghost**

'Hang on,' says Tod, 'are you implying
That there are Communists in Hell?'
'Where else?' John says. 'There's no denying
We seem to fit in pretty well;
The Party's used to persecution.
And, anyway, the Revolution
Continues after you are dead –
The flames of Hell are deepest red!'
'But surely there must be some friction
Twixt after-life and Marxist thought?'
'There are more things in heaven, old sport –
A surely greater contradiction
Is that you still condemn from birth
So many to a Hell on earth.'

He turns to King, 'Your lies and slander
Have gone on long enough. For years
You've dripped your poisonous propaganda
Into the sleeping public's ears.
You're nothing but a rotten twister;
I've no doubt you would sell your sister
To make a profit if you could.
You always were up to no good.
Your Liberty's a fairground racket
Ensuring that the world's too scared
To understand how it's been snared,
So folk like you can make a packet.
You talk of Freedom to disguise
The fact you've chained the world in lies.

**Rackstraw
makes a
speech**

67

You think the past is done and dusted;
And claim the world's one hope is dead;
You know tomorrow can't be trusted
Because you're scared the future's Red;
You're terrified of any movement
Committed to the world's improvement;
Your Liberty's a deadly game,
A tragic farce. In Freedom's name
Progressive freedoms are eroded
And dreams of justice are attacked,
Unless of course they come pre-packed,
Pre-paid, pro-West and colour-coded.
You prate of Freedom, but it's clear
For you best safety lies in fear.

Our generation was defeated.
What once was bright has lost its shine
Not least because of how it's treated
In books like yours, you lying swine.
Good God, man, you're a bloody viper.
They say the man who pays the piper
Can call the tune: who wrote the cheques
For you to spy on me and Rex?
Oh come on, Claud, don't go all silent,
You seem so good at naming names –'
'You've gone too far!' Claud King exclaims.
'Shut up – or else I might get violent –'
He puts a gun to Tod's sore head,
'And then the Author will be Dead!'

King has
heard
enough

68

Chapter 7

When in one line two crafts directly meet.
Hamlet III.4

'Don't shoot!' gasps Tod. 'Just shut the fuck up!'
Tod starts to cry. Fee starts to scream.
'Don't follow me,' King picks his book up,
'I'm not as gentle as I seem.'
'Of course,' says Rex, 'now take it easy,
You know how violence make me queasy.'
'Relax,' says Rackstraw, 'it's a bluff –'
'Don't think that I won't cut up rough!'
King flourishes the Smith and Wesson.
'If everyone will just stay calm,
Then Tod won't come to any harm.
I've no time for this history lesson.
I have a book to publicise,
Exposing you as Soviet spies'.

'Oh please don't tell us you're not staying,   **A shot**
When we've so much to talk about?'   **in the**
Tod mutters something like he's praying,   **dark**
But Rackstraw presses on. 'No doubt
We'll catch you later. Love and kisses.'
'You're History!' the old man hisses.
'Although it isn't what you meant,
I'll take that as a compliment.'
'For God's sake, Rackstraw, please don't push him –
Remember, you're already dead.
This gun is pointing at my head.'
'It isn't loaded, Tod. Let's rush him.'
As Rackstraw leaps, King screams 'Get back!'
The shooting starts. The room goes black.

King takes his chance and quickly legs it
Across the room and through the door.
John follows him towards the exit
While Tod slides slowly to the floor.
'Come on,' says John, 'we've got to find him!'
The Dedmans follow close behind him.
'Are you all right?' says Fee, 'Oh God!'
'Apparently he missed,' sobs Tod.
Inside the hall's a scene of anarchy:
Claud King is standing by the stair
And firing wildly in the air;
His PR team are looking panicky.
'Just think,' Tod gulps, 'I could have died!'
Fee takes his hand, 'my car's outside.'

The London streets are cold. It's raining.
Tod fears he's going to catch his death.
It's clear that he is not in training,
In fact, he's fat and scant of breath.
Fee's car's an ancient, battered Lada,
An enemy of back-seat ardour
With dodgy brakes and knackered clutch
That doesn't like Fee's driving much;
This means she has to start in second
And cannot ever get past third.
The battery's flat. 'This is absurd,'
Thinks Tod. But wait – he hasn't reckoned
With ghosts when they are in a rush.
'I say, do you chaps need a push?'

The dead are in dead good condition;
They push the banger while Fee steers.
'Try now!' Rex yells. 'Not the ignition!'
Fee grinds her way through both the gears
Until it jumps experimentally.
Three cars in front is King's old Bentley.
'That's him!' cries Trudi, 'CK1.'
'We're going to lose him!' 'Steady on!'
'Look, can't this thing go any faster?'
'Slow down! There's traffic lights ahead!'
Too late, they shoot the lights on red
And only just escape disaster,
A bus emerging from the right.
'Good Lord,' says Trudi, 'that was tight.'

The two cars speed across the city   **A car**
Like one of Tod's computer games,   **chase**
One's driven by back-seat committee,
The other by tormenting flames.
'I know a short-cut by the Palais.'
'Turn left!' 'No right!' 'Try down that alley.'
They speed on through pedestrian zones,
Knock down a line of traffic cones.
'Watch out!' 'Slow down! You'll hit that lorry.'
'O bloody hell! That's just our luck!
We're stuck behind a fucking truck –'
'There's ladies present, Tod.' 'I'm sorry.'
'John, don't be pompous,' Trudi says,
'It's how all writers talk these days.'

The Lada moves to undertake it.
The lorry swerves. Fee hits the brakes.
'Oh God! We're never going to make it!'
'Oh belt up Tod, for goodness sakes,
I know exactly what I'm doing.'
Road works ahead. No time for queuing.
'Down here!' says Rex. 'We'll cut him off.'
'Ahem,' Tod gives a nervous cough,
'I think that road-sign said No Entry.'
Fee executes a hand-brake turn –
The clutch complains, the brake-pads burn –
A neat, if somewhat rudimentary
Manoeuvre which is nicely lit
By bright blue lights. Police. 'Oh shit!'

'That's all we bloody need! Pull over!'   **A**
'Ignore them Fee, and concentrate   **proposal**
On catching King.' A large Range Rover
Is flashing them. 'Accelerate!'
'Righto!' Fee puts her foot down harder.
Tod watches as she drives the Lada,
Most beautified behind the wheel,
And knows he's been an imbecile.
He thinks about their stupid squabbles
And realizes there's a part
Of Fee still buried in his heart.
By now they're bouncing over cobbles
At nearly sixty. 'F-F-Fee,
W-will you m-m-marry me?'

But Fee's not heard him. Her attention
Is on the wheel. This journey's not
Improving the old car's suspension.
'S-speak up Tod, w-will I what?'
'I said, w-will you –' with a clatter
They hit the tarmac. 'Doesn't matter.'
The Bentley's still three cars in front.
Meanwhile, the back-seat ghosts confront
The issue of Ms Dedman's virtue.
'Look Rex, please don't misunderstand
What you've just heard at second hand.
I'm sorry if this news has hurt you,
But now it's out, I'm glad you know
I once loved Trudi, long ago.'

John turns to Trudi, 'Dear, I couldn't
Have loved you if I ever thought
That I'd come home. A soldier shouldn't
Expose himself in case he's caught.
But Love's another kind of duty,
My colours were your grace and beauty.
And when a chap's against the wall
Then Love makes cowards of us all.
When we were told to take The Pimple,
With death a chance of one in five,
I knew that I might not survive.
Because I loved you, death was simple.
Love's dialectic is a test,
And, though I failed, I did my best.

**An
explanation**

73

We had the chance when we were younger
To overthrow the ancient reign
Of poverty, despair and hunger.
The battle-lines were drawn in Spain.
It was our choice, and our decision,
As Communists we shared a vision
That Freedom's just an empty word
While Justice struggles to be heard
(And when it is, they call it treason!)
In Spain, for once, the choice was stark:
Between the armies of the dark
And those of Freedom, Light and Reason.
We fought and died to keep that light
From falling into endless night.'

He stares out at the midnight weather.
The London streets go slashing by.
'I'm glad to see you're still together,
That love survives us when we die.
You may think this is special pleading
But I can still remember reading
Some lines Rex wrote in '38:
"When Life goes underground to wait
Love must be metal, iron as Winter,
As secret as the earth in snow
Until the rebel Spring shall grow
And pavements crack and Empires splinter.
Then we shall breathe the air above
Of Liberty and Human Love."

I thought of that when I was lying
Out on that Spanish hill with King.
By then I knew that I was dying
And wouldn't see another Spring,
And yet in my imagination
The Springs of human liberation,
Of comradeship and loving toil
Were planted in that Spanish soil.
There was a farmhouse in the distance,
Protected by a little wood;
Because I'd lost a lot of blood;
King said he'd try to get assistance
Before the Fascists could attack.
Of course, I knew he'd not be back.'

'But is it true about old Warty,
Or was that just a clever guess?'
'Well, snooping always was his forte,
But if it was for SIS
Or OSS it doesn't matter
(Though I suspect it was the latter).
What's certain is King's later role
At IRD, the tight control
He exercised on British culture,
Especially in the long Cold War.
You don't think *Nineteen Eighty-Four*
Was written by that creeping vulture
I knew at school? It now appears
That King was ghosting him for years.'

While they've been nattering intently
Fee's turned into a lorry park.
Ahead of them is King's old Bentley,
Its engine purring in the dark.
'He can't escape,' shouts Rex, enraptured,
'There's no way out, the bastard's captured.
At last we've got the stupid bleed-'
When with a sudden roar of speed
The Bentley sprints in their direction;
Fee slams the brakes on. Nothing. 'Fuck!'
'Try changing gear!' 'I can't! It's stuck!'
Tod grabs the wheel in self-protection.
Too late, as with a blinding flash
They meet head-on. A hideous crash.

It's clear there can be no survivors.
The sulphurous and tormenting flames
Deter all bids to reach the drivers,
Who, giving up the flesh's claims,
Are left to melt in their own fire,
An emblem of the world's desire,
Of anger's heat and love's decay.
The sheeted dead are wheeled away.
Good night sweet Prince. Goodnight sweet Ladies.
It's almost time to end this tale
Of madness, poison and betrayal;
Our characters are off to Hades,
The dreary plains of asphodel
Where henceforth each of them must dwell…

...It's hellish dark. The smell of burning. **Tod in the**
The gnash of teeth. Some human screams. **underworld**
The grind of mill-wheels slowly turning.
'It's not as awful as it seems,'
Rex beams, 'just takes some getting used to.
I'll make sure that you're introduced to
My old friend Virgil – he can show
You all the ropes – and chains (ho ho!).
But first,' Rex points towards a table,
'It seems some chaps have all the luck –
Your punishment's to write a book!'
Not for the first time in this fable
Our hero wishes he were dead –
Then realises what he's said.

'For God's sake Tod, don't look so hateful.
I've had to pull a lot of strings
To get you this – you should be grateful.
Perhaps you'd like the usual Slings
And Arrows course (includes free Stoning)?
I thought not. So, let's stop this moaning.
I'm sure you'll crack on once it's clear
There's fuck-all else to do round here.'
Tod sits, but tries to look disdainful,
'Er – why are all the ink pots red?'
'A little joke. You've often said
Biography's so bloody painful;
I rather thought my new Life should
Be written in the author's blood.'

'Your *Life*?' Tod's words explode with feeling,
'You'll get one over my dead bod –'
'Quite so. It might be more appealing
If it was done in verse, eh Tod?
What Russians call a *roman stihi*.
I understand they're devilish tricky,
Especially if you have to rhyme,
But it might help to pass the time.
"The Devil will find work for idle –"
Oh one more thing – it must be done
In Pushkin sonnets. Well, have fun.
Try not to look so suicidal!'
Rex disappears into the night.
Tod takes a pen and starts to write…

… The picture fades. Cue railway creaking,
French landscape shot in monochrome,
Three Englishmen, afraid of speaking
Of their adventure far from home.
One seems to find the whole thing boring.
One's fast asleep and calmly snoring.
The third is staring into space,
A stern expression on his face.
'Are you all right, John? You're not blinking.'
John smiles: 'The Struggle's like this train
That's taking us to fight in Spain.
We can't get off, it's no good thinking
This is a holiday, eh Rex?'
Rex shuts his eyes and thinks of sex…

Acknowledgements

One stanza's left to roll the credits:
So little room to list the names
Of all those friends whose careful edits
Helped save this novel from the flames,
To thank the readers of these pages
Back in the messy, first-draft stages
When, frankly, things weren't going well –
Viz Gordon Hodgeon, Richard Kell,
Mike 'Brummie' Wilson, Cynthia Fuller,
George Jowett, Anna Tsernovitch.
For polishing a typescript which
Would otherwise have been much duller,
I owe you more than I can cram
In this last line by way of – Damn!

Notes

Chapter 1

YCL	Young Communist League.
Daily Worker	Daily paper of the British Communist Party, now the *Morning Star.*
The Glue Pot	Affectionate name for the George, the pub on Great Portland Street where writers could cash BBC cheques.

Chapter 2

'*O soave fanciulla*'	'Oh lovely girl', from Puccini's opera *La Bohème*.
L'Humanité	Daily newspaper of the French Communist Party.
Hill 481	In July 1938 the British Battalion of the International Brigades attempted to capture Hill 481, a key position in the Battle of the Ebro. The hill was well protected with barbed wire, trenches and bunkers. After suffering heavy casualties, the British were forced to retreat. A few weeks later the surviving International Brigades were withdrawn from Spain.

Chapter 3

Gordon Herickx	British sculptor.
'Gabe'	'Gabriel' was the pen-name of *Daily Worker* cartoonist James Friel.
André Malraux and Ralph Bates	Authors of best-selling novels set in 1930's Spain, notably *L'Espoir* and *The Olive Field*

Chapter 4

Harry Pollitt	Legendary General Secretary of the British Communist Party.

Chapter 5

King Street	Headquarters of the British Communist Party near Covent Garden.
Harry	Harry Pollitt (see above).
Ted Bramley	Popular London District Secretary of the Communist Party.
Unity	Unity Theatre was a left-wing theatre in London.
Johnny Campbell	Assistant editor of the *Daily Worker*.
Inprecorr	International Press Correspondence, the weekly journal of the Communist International.

Chapter 7

The Pimple	Nickname for Hill 481.
SIS	Secret Intelligence Service, later MI6.
OSS	Office of Strategic Services, later the CIA
IRD	Information Research Department, black-propaganda organization attached to the Foreign Office.

Also available from Five Leaves

Not Just a Game: sporting poetry
Edited by Andy Croft and Sue Dymoke
225 pages, 978 1 905512 13 3, £9.99 paperback

From the first length to the final frame, from Jack Hobbs to Brian Clough, from Centre Court to the Great North Run, *Not Just a Game* captures the tension and the laughter, the pain and the pleasure, and the blood sweat and tears. A unique archive of sporting life – from angling to boxing, from swimming to tennis, from cricket to football and back again, and from skittleball to hang-gliding as recorded by UA Fanthorpe, Ted Hughes, Seamus Heaney, PG Wodehouse, John Arlott and many more.

Speaking English
Edited by Andy Croft
194 pages, 978 1 905512 12 6, £9.99 paperback

Speaking English brings together over a hundred different poets from four continents – including John Hartley Williams, Jamie McKendrick, Blake Morrison, Robert Nye, Tom Paulin, Peter Porter, Deryn Rees-Jones, Anne Stevenson, Matthew Sweeney and George Szirtes – to celebrate the seventieth birthday of the prolific critic, editor, publisher and poet John Lucas. *Speaking English* celebrates common experience, the regional and the radical, the demotic and the democratic, the poetics of saying what you mean and the politics of meaning what you say.

**All Five Leaves titles are available
post free in the UK from
www.inpressbooks.co.uk**